The Kew Gardens
FLOWERING PLANTS
COLOURING BOOK

*Over 40 beautiful illustrations
plus colour guides*

ARCTURUS

All illustrations included in this book have been taken from the Library, Art & Archives Collections of the Royal Botanic Gardens, Kew.

Special thanks to Lynn Parker, Art and Illustrations Curator, and Dr Martyn Rix, Editor of *Curtis's Botanical Magazine*.

ARCTURUS

This edition published in 2016 by Arcturus Publishing Limited
26/27 Bickels Yard, 151–153 Bermondsey Street,
London SE1 3HA

ISBN: 978-1-78404-561-6
CH004519UK
Supplier 37, Date 0516, Print Run 5416

Printed in Romania

Created for children 10+

Introduction

The artworks presented here are taken from the archive of *Curtis's Botanical Magazine*, the longest-running periodical featuring colour illustrations of plants in the world. Founded in 1787 by apothecary and botanist William Curtis (1746–99) as *The Botanical Magazine*, it appealed to scientists as well as ladies and gentlemen wanting information on the many newly introduced ornamental flowers that were in vogue in the gardens of the wealthy and fashionable. The 19th century saw a proliferation of plant collecting, with new species being sought out to satisfy the Victorian craze for the unusual and exotic.

Each issue of the magazine contained three hand-coloured copper-engraved plates alongside the text, which described the Linnaean name, genus and qualities, along with botanical, horticultural and historical background, associated information relating to what we might now call conservation, and any economic applications or uses. Curtis charged one shilling per month and soon had 2,000 subscribers. Accomplished artists were commissioned to produce the plates, and the magazine was an instant success. The plates continued to be hand-coloured until 1948, when a scarcity of colourists led to the implementation of photographic reproduction.

The name of the magazine was changed to *Curtis's Botanical Magazine* after Curtis's death in 1799. It was first produced at Kew in 1841, when William Jackson Hooker (1785–1865) moved south from Glasgow University to become Director of the Royal Botanic Gardens. Joseph Dalton Hooker (1817–1911) took over the role of editor from his father in 1865, and the magazine has continued to be produced by Kew Gardens' staff and artists to this day.

All of the artworks included here are by Walter Hood Fitch (1817–92), who illustrated more than 2,700 plants for the magazine and published over 10,000 illustrations during his career. Fitch's exceptional talent had been recognized by the Glasgow mill owner to whom he was apprenticed as a pattern drawer at the age of thirteen. An introduction to the then editor and sole illustrator of *Curtis's Magazine,* William Hooker, led to the young Fitch moving to Kew in 1841 when William was appointed Director of the Royal Botanic Gardens. A dispute with Joseph, William's son, led to Fitch's resignation in 1877. After leaving Kew, Fitch remained a sought after botanical artist.

Presented here are 44 colour plates of hardy plants together with their corresponding black and white lithographs for you to try your hand at colouring. The original watercolour drawings were made from life, so you can be sure that your finished renderings are based on accurate and precise representations of the actual plants. A key to the plates, using plant names given at the time of publication, can be found overleaf. The current names of those now obsolete can usually be found on the Internet, and you may even discover a reference to the original plate.

Key: List of plates

1 *Disa grandiflora*

2 *Impatiens repens*

3 *Grindelia grandiflora*

4 *Lilium roseum*

5 *Primula cortusoides*

6. *Gilia lutea*

7 *Camellia rosaeflora*

8 *Aucuba japonica*

9 *Rosa sericea*

10 *Chrysanthemum carinatum*

11 *Impatiens flaccida*

12 *Echinacea angustifolia*

13 *Rhodanthe manglesii*

14 *Lewisia rediviva*

15 *Clomenocoma montana*

16 *Nolana lanceolata*

17 *Philadelphus hirsutus*

18 *Lilium auratum*

19 *Hibiscus huegelii*

20 *Vieussieuxia fugax*

21 *Desmodium skinneri*

22 *Micranthella candollei*

23 *Meconopsis aculeata*

24 *Delphinium brunonianum*

25 *Thladiantha dubia*

26 *Darwinia fimbriata*

27 *Aquilegia caerulea*

28 *Acmena floribunda*

29 *Sparaxis pulcherrima*

30 *Passiflora van-volxemii*

31 *Haemanthus tenuiflorus*

32 *Plagianthus lyallii*

33 *Gilia achillaeafolia*

34 *Meconopsis nipalensis*

35 *Iris junceum*

36 *Salvia rubescens*

37 *Pyrus prunifolia*

38 *Fritillaria tulipifolia*

39 *Scorzonera undulata*

40 *Crocus byzantinus*

41 *Primula parryi*

42 *Tulipa orphanidea*

43 *Tulipa eichleri*

44 *Coelogyne hookeriana*

4073.

W. Fitch del.

Pub by S. Curtis Glazenwood Essex, March 1.1844

Swan Sc.

W. Fitch del.   Pub. by S. Curtis Glazenwood Essex, March 1.1844.   Swan Sc.

4073.

Fitch, del. et lith.

R. B & R, imp.

4404.

Fitch, del et lith.

R, B & R, imp.

4628

Fitch del et lith.

Reeve & Nichols, imp.

1.   2.   3.

Fitch del et lith.   Reeve & Nichols, imp.

3

2

1.

Fitch del. et lith.

F. Reeve imp.

Fitch. del. et lith.

F. Reeve imp.

W. Fitch, del. et lith.

Vincent Brooks, Imp.

W. Fitch, del. et lith.

1.

2.

Vincent Brooks, Imp.

Fitch, del et. lith.

F. Reeve, imp.

Fitch, del et lith.

F. Reeve, imp.

5044.

1. 5044.

W. Fitch del. et lith.

Vincent Brooks Imp.

1.

5512.

W.Fitch, del.et lith.

Vincent Brooks, Imp.

5200.

9

W. Fitch, del. et lith.

Vincent Brooks, Imp

W. Fitch del. et lith.

Vincent Brooks, Imp.

W. Fitch del. et lith.

Vincent Brooks, Imp.

W.Fitch,del.et.lith.

Vincent Brooks,Imp.

W. Fitch, del et lith.

Vincent Brooks, Imp

5281.

W. Fitch, del. et lith.

Vincent Brooks, Imp.

W. Fitch, del. et lith.

Vincent Brooks, Imp.

5290.

5290.

5395.

W. Fitch, del. et lith.

Vincent Brooks, Imp.

5395.

W. Fitch, del. et lith.

Vincent Brooks, Imp.

1

2

3

4

5310.

W.Fitch, del.et lith.

Vincent Brooks, Imp.

5310.

W.Fitch, del.et lith.

Vincent Brooks, Imp.

5027.

W. Fitch, del. et lith.

Vincent Brooks, Imp.

1.

2.

W. Fitch, del. et lith.

Vincent Brooks, Imp.

5034

W.Fitch,del.et lith.

Vincent Brooks,Imp

W. Fitch, del. et lith.

Vincent Brooks, Imp

5338.

W. Fitch, del. et lith.

Vincent Brooks, Imp.

Vincent Brooks, Imp.

5406.

W.Fitch, del et lith.

Vincent Brooks, Imp.

5438.

W. Fitch, del. et lith.

Vincent Brooks, Imp.

5452.

W.Fitch,del.et lith.

Vincent Brooks,Imp.

5452.

W.Fitch,del.et lith.

Vincent Brooks,Imp.

W. Fitch, del . et lith .

Vincent Brooks, Imp.

W. Fitch, del. et lith.

Vincent Brooks, Imp.

5456.

W. Fitch, del et lith.

Vincent Brooks, Imp.

W. Fitch, del. et lith.

Vincent Brooks, Imp.

5461.

W. Fitch, del. et lith.

Vincent Brooks, Imp.

W. Fitch, del. et lith.

Vincent Brooks, Imp.

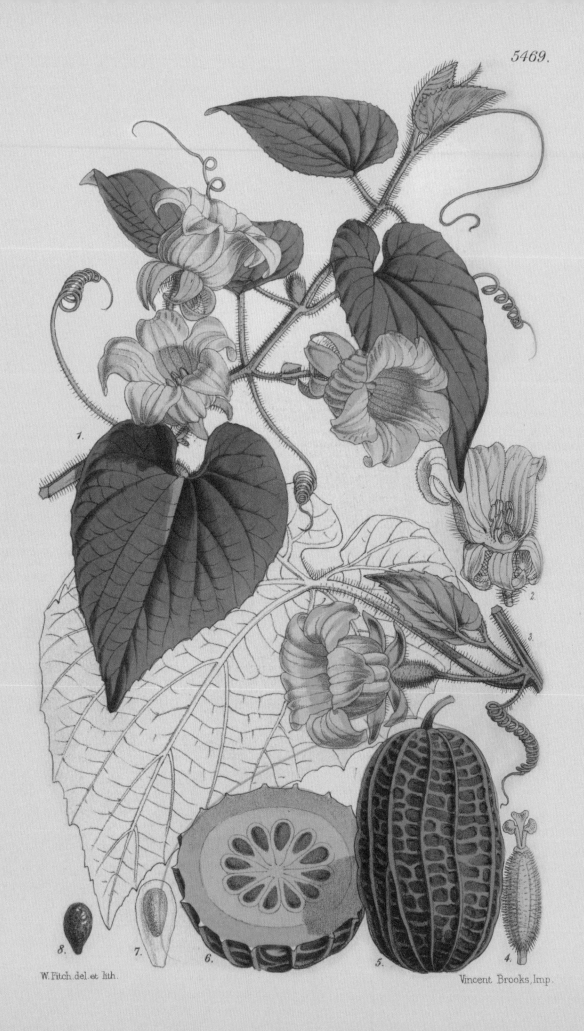

5469.

W. Fitch. del. et lith.

Vincent Brooks, Imp.

W. Fitch del. et lith.

Vincent Brooks, Imp.

4.

5.

1.

2.

3.

W. Fitch, del. et lith.

Vincent Brooks, Imp.

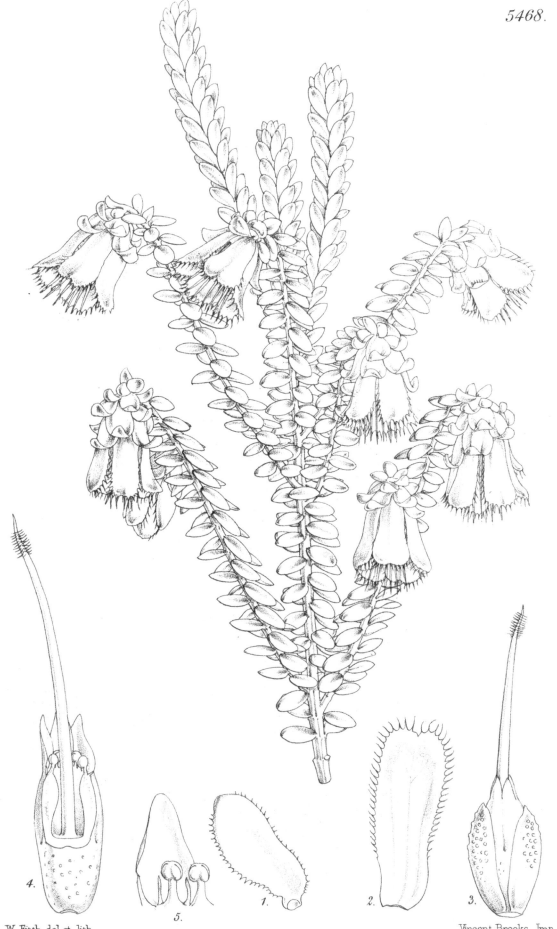

4.   5.   1.   2.   3.

W. Fitch, del. et lith.   Vincent Brooks, Imp.

5477.

1.

W. Fitch, del. et lith.

Vincent Brooks, Imp.

1.

W. Fitch, del. et lith.

Vincent Brooks, Imp.

5480.

W.Fitch, del. et lith.

Vincent Brooks, Imp.

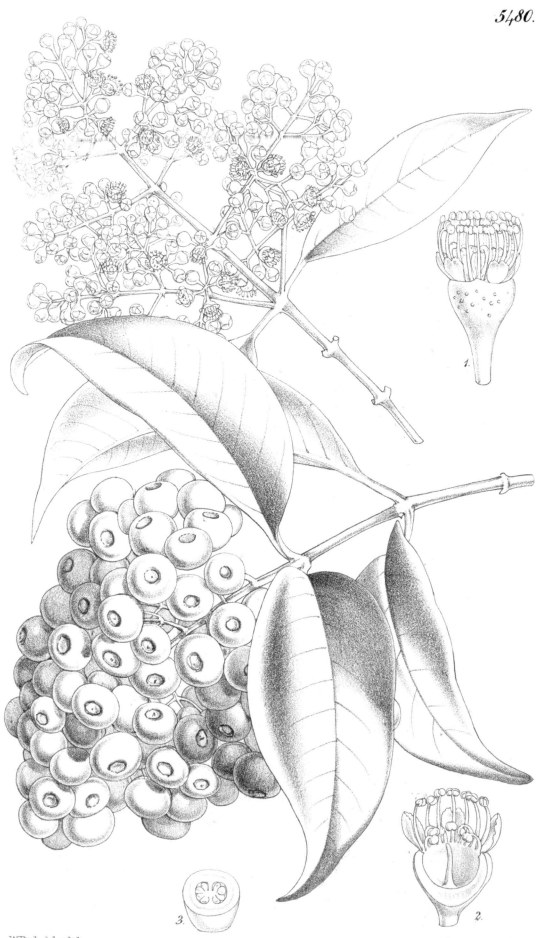

5480.

W. Fitch, del. et lith.

Vincent Brooks, Imp.

1.

2.

3.

5555.

W. Fitch, del. et lith.

Vincent Brooks, Imp.

5571.

W.Fitch, del.et lith.

Vincent Brooks, Imp.

W. Fitch, del. et lith.

Vincent Brooks, Imp.

5881.

W. Fitch, del. et lith.

Vincent Brooks, Day & Son, Imp.

1.

2.

3.

W. Fitch, del. et lith.

Vincent Brooks, Day & Son, Imp.

5935.

W. Fitch, del. et lith.

Vincent Brooks, Day & Son, Imp.

W. Fitch, del. et lith.

Vincent Brooks, Day & Son, Imp.

5939.

W. Fitch, del. et lith.

Vincent Brooks, Day & Son, Imp.

5585.

W.Fitch del. et lith.

Vincent Brooks Imp.

1.

1.

Vincent Brooks, Day & Son, Imp.

5947

W.Fitch, del et lith.

Vincent.Brooks Day & Son,Imp

W.Fitch, del et lith.

Vincent Brooks Day & Son Imp

6158.

1.

W Fitch, del et Lith.

Vincent Brooks Day & Son Imp

5969.

W.Fitch, del et lith.

Vincent Brooks Day & Son, Imp.

W. Fitch, del et lith.

Vincent Brooks Day & Son, Imp.

W. Fitch, del et lith

Vincent Brooks Day & Son, imp.

W.Fitch, del et lith.

Vincent Brooks Day & Son, Imp.

1

2

1

2

W.Fitch, del et.lith.

Vincent.Brooks Day & Son,Imp.

W. Fitch del et lith

Vincent Brooks Day & Son Imp

W.Fitch del et lith

Vincent Brooks Day & Son Imp

W.Fitch, del. et lith.

Vincent Brooks Day & Son Imp.

W. Fitch, del. et lith.

Vincent Brooks Day & Son Imp.

W.Fitch, del.et lith.

Vincent Brooks,Day & Son,Imp.

W. Fitch, del. et lith.

Vincent Brooks, Day & Son, Imp.

6388.

1.

2.

F.H.W. del. J. Nugent Fitch Lith.

Vincent Brooks Day & Son Imp.

6388.

1.

2.

F.H.W. del. J.Nugent Fitch Lith.

Vincent Brooks Day & Son Imp